-1507
4422
1.25
SSAA, String Orchestra and Organ
MAGNIFICAT
Niccola Porpora
MANHATTANVILLE
COLLEGE
Choral Series
Ralph Hunter, editor
MARKS MUSIC CORPORATION
136 W. 52nd St., New York, N. Y. 10019
Printed in U. S. A.

Manhattanville College Choral Series

MAGNIFICAT

SSAA, String Orchestra and Organ*

NICCOLA PORPORA

Edited by
RALPH HUNTER

Niccola Antonio Porpora was born in Naples, August 17, 1686, and died there, March 3, 1768. At the age of ten he entered the Conservatorio dei Poverie de Gesu Christe at Naples where he was a student of Gaetano Greco, Matteo Biordano and Ottavio Campanile. During a long life dedicated to composition, performance and teaching (Joseph Haydn was one of his voice students), Porpora composed 44 operas, 11 oratorios and numerous masses and motets. In 1733 he was engaged by the directors of the "Opera of the Nobility" in London which had been organized as a rival company to that of George Frideric Handel.

During the period from 1726 to 1739 Porpora was engaged as a teacher of music by the "Ospedali degli Incurabili", one of four famous Venetian orphanages renowned for their high level of musical performance. The orchestras and choirs of these asylums were composed of girl inmates. The "Magnificat" was composed for the aforementioned orphanage and received its first performance there.

*Score and Parts available on rental

EDWARD B. MARKS MUSIC CORPORATION
136 West 52nd Street New York, N. Y. 10019

Magnificat

SSAA, String Orchestra and Organ *

1. Magnificat anima mea

Duration: *ca.* 9 min.

NICCOLA PORPORA (1686-1767)
edited by Ralph Hunter

* score and parts available on rental
** for performance without orchestra

2. Et exultavit

* All solos may be sung by a few sopranos.

S I: me - o ex - sul - ta - vit, ex - sul - ta - vit.
B
f Tutti
S I: qui - a re - spe - xit hu - mi - li - ta - - tem an -
S II: qui - a re - spe - xit hu - mi - li - ta - - tem an -
A I: qui - a re - spe - xit hu - mi - li - ta - - tem an -
A II: qui - a re - spe - xit hu - mi - li - ta - - tem an -

tr
cil-lae, an-cil-lae su - ae, re - spe - xit hu-mi-li-
cil-lae, an - cil-lae su - ae, re - spe - xit hu-mi-li-
cil-lae, an - cil - lae su - ae, hu-mi-li - ta-tem
cil-lae, an - cil - lae su - ae, hu-mi-li - ta-tem
ta - tem an - cil-lae, an-cil-lae su - ae.
ta - tem an - cil-lae, an-cil-lae su - ae.
hu-mi-li - ta-tem an - cil-lae, an-cil-lae su - ae.
hu-mi-li - ta-tem an - cil-lae, an-cil-lae su - ae.

C
Solo
I
S
II
Ec - ce _ e - nim ex hoc, _ Ec - ce _ e - nim ex hoc be-
Solo
I
A
II
Ec - ce _ e - nim ex hoc, _ Ec - ce _ e - nim ex hoc be-
C
(p)
(f)
p
a - tam me di - cent, me di - cent, be - a - tam me di - cent o - mnes,
f Tutti
(Tutti)
Be - a - tam me di cent o - mnes,
a - tam me di - cent, me di - cent, be - a - tam me di - cent o - mnes,
Be - a - tam me di - cent o - mnes,
f

o - mnes ge - ne - ra - ti - o - - -
o - mnes ge - ne - ra - ti - o - - -
o - mnes ge - ne - ra - ti - o - - -
o - mnes ge - ne - ra - ti - o - - -
tr
tr
tr
- - - - nes,
- - - - nes,
- - - - nes,
- - - - nes,
tr
tr

tr
Solo
tr
Tutti
I
S
II
ge - ne - ra - ti - o - nes, me di - cent be -
ge - ne - ra - ti - o - nes, be -
Solo
Tutti
I
A
II
ge - ne - ra - ti - o - nes, me di - cent be -
ge - ne - ra - ti - o - nes, be -
tr
Solo
tr
Tutti
a - tam, be - a - tam me di - cent o - mnes ge - ne -
a - tam, me di - cent o - mnes ge - ne -
Solo
tr
Tutti
a - tam, be - a - tam me di - cent o - mnes ge - ne -
a - tam, me di - cent o - mnes ge - ne -

D
tr
Solo p
ra - ti - o - nes. Qui - a fe - cit
Solo p
ra - ti - o - nes. Qui - a fe - cit
ra - ti - o - nes.
ra - ti - o - nes.
D
p
tr
Tutti f
mi - hi ma - gna; Qui po - tens
Tutti f
mi - hi ma - gna; Qui po - tens
(Tutti) f
Qui po - tens est,
(Tutti) f
Qui po - tens est,
f

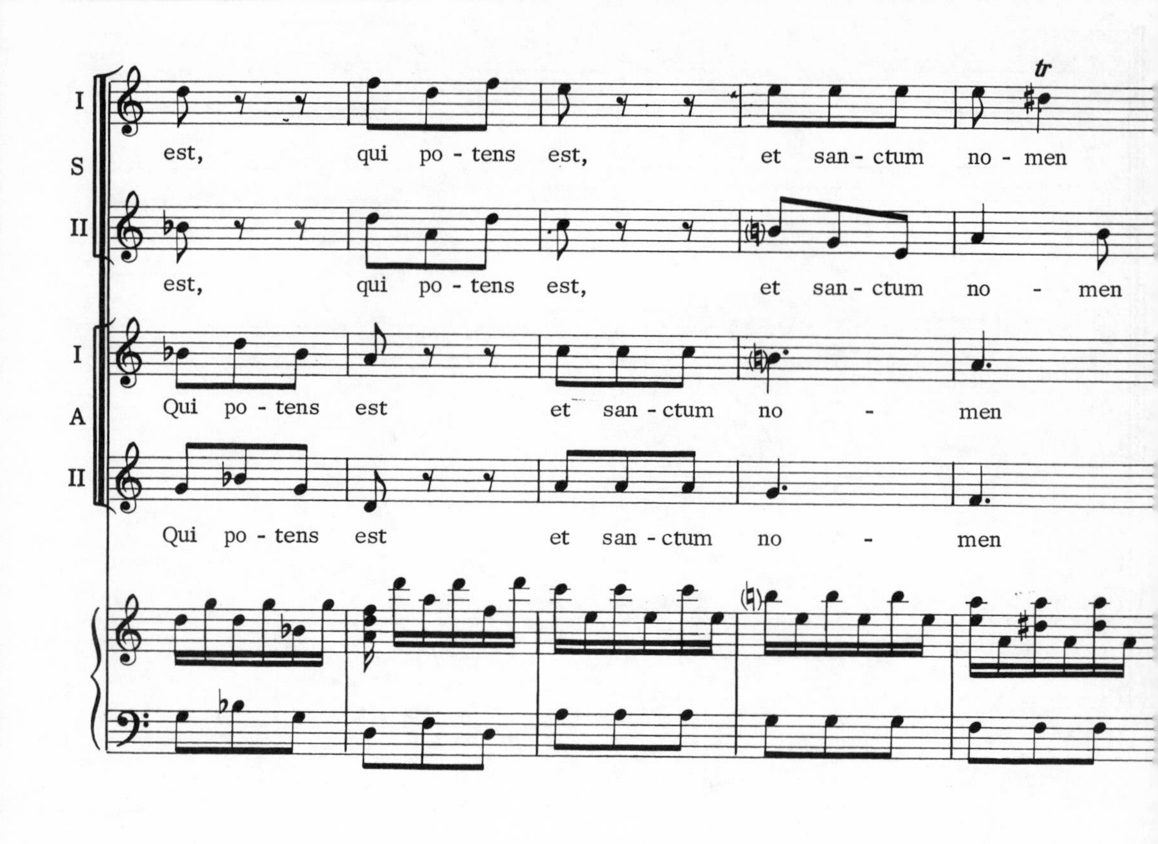
I
S
II
I
A
II
est,
qui po - tens est,
et san - ctum no - men
Qui po - tens est
et san - ctum no - men

cresc.
e

tr
jus, san - ctum no - - men
jus, san - ctum no - men
tr
jus, san - ctum no - - men
jus, san - ctum no - men
tr
e - jus.
e - jus.
e - jus.
e - jus.

3. Et misericordia

I
S
II
I
A
II
sempre cresc.
ge - ni-es ti-men - - -
sempre cresc.
- ni-es ti - men - -
sempre cresc.
- - ni-es ti-men - - - ti-bus
sempre cresc.
- ni-es ti - men - - - ti-bus
sempre cresc.
- ti-bus e - - -
- ti-bus e - - -
e - - -
e - - -

I
S
II
I
A
II
um, ti - men - ti-bus
um, ti - men - ti-bus
um, ti - men - ti-bus
um, ti - men - ti-bus
mp
dim.
rall.
e - - um.
pp

4. Fecit potentiam

I
S
II
I
A
II
- - sit su - per - bos, su - per - bos men - te
- - sit su - per - bos, su - per - bos men - te
- - sit su - per - bos, su - per - bos men te
- - sit su - per - bos, su - per - bos men - te

I
S
II
I
A
II
cor - dis, cor - dis su - i.
cor - dis, men - te cor - dis su - i.
cor - dis, men - te cor - dis su - i.
cor - dis, men - te cor - dis su - i.

A
I
S
II
I
A
II
De - po - - - su-it, de-po - -
De - po - - su-it, de-po - -
De - po - - - su-it, de-po - -
De - po - - su-it, de-po - -
A
- su-it po-ten-tes de se - de, et
- su-it po-ten-tes de se-de, de se-de,
- su-it po-ten-tes de se-de, de se-de, et ex-al-
- su-it po-ten-tes de se-de, de se-de,

I
S
II
— ex - al - ta - - - vit, ex - al -
et ex - al - ta - - - vit, ex - al -
I
A
II
ta - - - vit, ex - al -
et ex - al - ta - - vit, ex - al -
B
ta - vit hu - mi - les. E - su - ri - en - tes im -
ta - vit hu - mi - les. E - su - ri - en - tes
ta - vit hu - mi - les. E - su - ri -
ta - vit hu - mi - les. E - su - ri - en - tes

I
S
II
ple - vit bo - - nis et di-vi-tes di -
im-ple - vit bo - nis, im-ple - vit bo - nis et
I
A
II
en - tes im - ple - vit, im-ple - vit bo - nis et
im-ple - vit bo - nis, im-ple - vit bo - nis et
tr
I
S
II
mi - sit in a - - - -
di-vi-tes di - mi - sit in a - - -
I
A
II
di-vi-tes di - mi - sit in a - - -
di-vi-tes di - mi - sit in a - - -

I
S
II
I
A
II
- - - nes, in a - nes.
- - - nes, in a - nes.
- - - nes, in a - nes.
- - - nes, in a - nes.
tr
C
Su-sce-pit Is-ra-el, Su-sce-pit Is-ra-el, pu-e-rum, pu-e-rum
Su-sce-pit Is-ra-el, Su-sce-pit Is-ra-el, pu-e-rum, pu-e-rum
Su-sce-pit Is-ra-el, Su-sce-pit Is-ra-el, pu-e-rum, pu-e-rum
Su-sce-pit Is-ra-el, Su-sce-pit Is-ra-el, pu-e-rum, pu-e-rum

dolce
mf
dim.
I
S
II
su - um, re-cor - da - tus mi - se - ri -
su - um,
mf dolce
dim.
I
A
II
su - um, re-cor - da - - - tus
su - um,
mf
dim.
cresc.
cor - di-ae, mi - se - ri - cor - - -
cresc.
mi - se - ri - cor - - -
cresc.

D
mf
f
I
S
II
A
di - ae su - ae, re - cor -
re - cor - da - tus mi -
di - ae su - ae, re - cor -
re - cor - da - tus mi -
da - tus mi - se - ri - cor - di - ae
se - ri - cor - di - ae
da - tus mi - se - ri - cor - di - ae
se - ri - cor - di - ae
tr

I
S
II
I
A
II
tr
su - ae; Si - cut lo - cu - tus est ad
su - ae; Si - cut lo - cu - tus, lo - cu - tus est ad
su - ae; Si - cut lo - cu - tus est ad
su - ae; Si - cut lo - cu - tus, lo - cu - tus est — ad
pa - tres no - stros, ad pa - tres no - stros A -
pa - tres no - stros, ad pa - tres no - stros A -
pa - tres no - stros, ad pa - tres no - stros A -
pa - tres no - stros, ad pa - tres no - stros A -

E
I
S
II
I
A
II
- - - bra-ham et se - mi-ni
- - - bra - ham et se - mi-ni e -
- - - bra-ham et se - mi-ni e -
- - - bra-ham et se - mi-ni
E
tr
e - jus, et se - mi-ni e - jus in sae - -
- - - jus in sae - -
- - - jus in sae - -
e - jus et se - mi - ni e - jus in sae -

I
S
II
I
A
II
- cu - la, in sae - cu - la.
- - cu - la, in sae - cu - la.
- - cu - la, in sae - cu - la.
- - cu - la, in sae - cu - la.
tr
tr

5. Gloria Patri

I
S
II
I
A
II
rall.
ri - a,
Glo - ri - a.
ri - a, Glo - ri - a.
ri-a, Glo - ri-a.
ri - a,
Glo - ri - a.
tr
tr
tr

6. Sicut erat

Allegro (♩. = 72)
mp
Si - cut e - rat in prin - ci - pi - o et nunc et
Si - cut e - rat in prin - ci - pi - o et nunc et
Allegro (♩. = 72)
nunc et sem - per nunc et sem - per et in
nunc et sem - per nunc et sem - per et in
et in sae-cu-la sae -
et in
A
tr
f
cresc.

I
S
II
I
A
II
sae-cu-la sae - cu - lo - rum, A - -
sae - cu - la sae - cu - lo - rum, A - -
- - cu - lo - rum, A - - -
sae-cu-la sae - cu - lo - rum, A - -
tr

I
S
II
I
A
II
tr
tr
tr
I
S
II
I
A
II

I
S
II
I
A
II
men, A - men, A -
men, A - men, A -
men, A - men, A -
men, A - men, A -

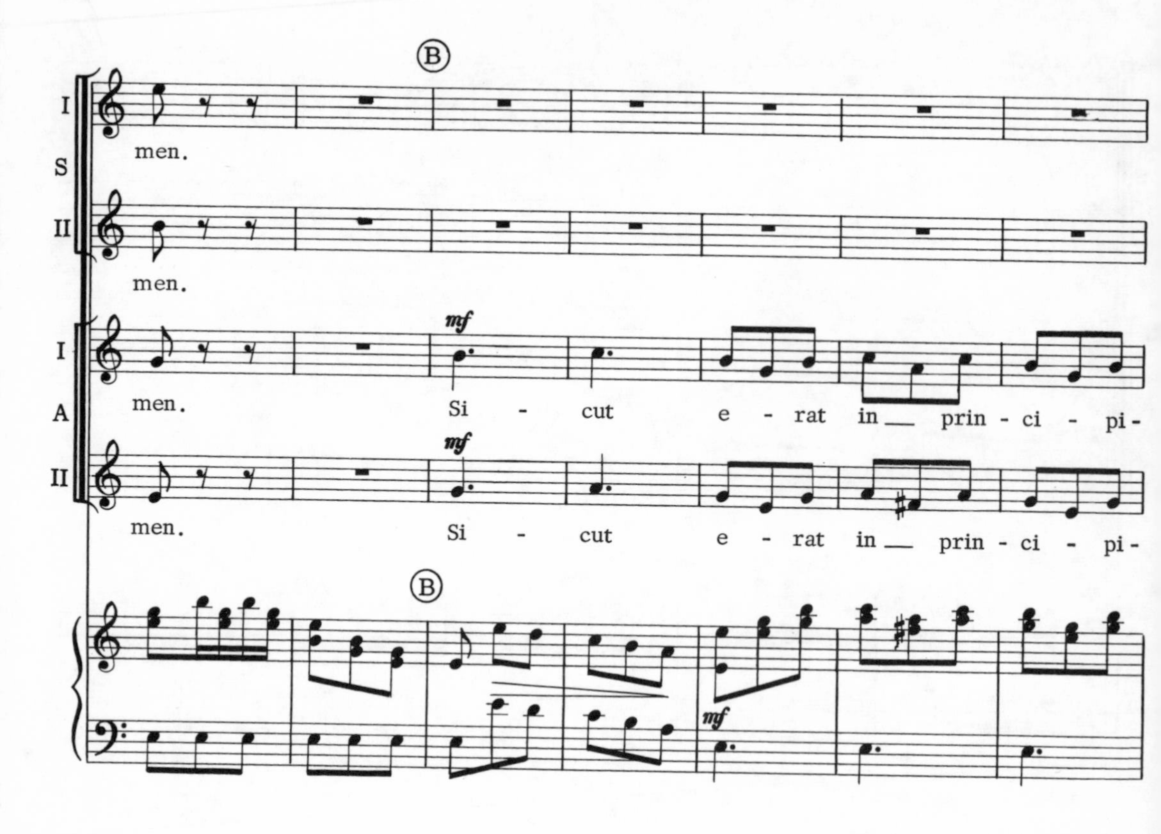
B
I
S
II
I
A
II
mf
men.
men.
men.
Si - cut e - rat in prin - ci - pi -
men.
Si - cut e - rat in prin - ci - pi -
B
mf

I
S
II
I
A
II
tr
cresc.
o et nunc et nunc et sem - per, nunc et sem -
o et nunc et nunc et sem - per, nunc et sem -
cresc.

I
S
II
A
Si - cut e - rat in prin - ci - pi - o et nunc, et
nunc et sem - per, nunc et sem - per
nunc et sem - per, nunc et sem - per et
per, et in sae - cu - la
per, et in
C

I
S
II
I
A
II
et in sae-cu-la sae - cu - lo - rum,
in sae-cu-la sae - cu - lo - rum,
sae - - cu - lo - rum, A -
sae - cu-la sae - cu - lo - rum, A - -
(tr)
A -
A -
tr

D
I
S
II
tr
men, A -
I
A
II
men, A -
men, A -
D
tr

I
S
II
I
A
II
men, A
Adagio
ff
div.
men, A - men, A - men,
A - men.

3 1303 00057 4385